A BOOK ABOUT
OCD

BY
HOLLY DUHIG

BookLife
PUBLISHING

©2018
BookLife Publishing
King's Lynn
Norfolk PE30 4LS

A catalogue record for this book is available from the British Library.

ISBN: 978-1-78637-344-1

Written by:
Holly Duhig

Edited by:
Madeline Tyler

Designed by:
Danielle Jones

With grateful thanks to Place2Be for their endorsement of this series.

These titles have been developed to support teachers and school counsellors in exploring pupils' mental health, and have been reviewed and approved by the clinical team at Place2Be, the leading national children's mental health charity.

PHOTOCREDITS

Front Cover – kostudio. 4 – Daisy Daisy, pecaphoto77. 5 – mimagephotography, Olimpik. 6 – Mita Stock Images. 7 – Bukavik .8 –pathdoc, gerasimov_foto_174. 9 – Borysevych.com, chainarong06. 10 –11 – Bukavik. 12 – Photographee. eu, Carla Francesca Castagno. 13 – CREATISTA. 14 – Halfpoint, Dudarev Mikhail. 15 – Iakov Filimonov, Marco Brockmann, Rocketclips, Inc.. 16 – Bukavik. 17 – Darren Baker, eggeegg, Alexey Rotanov. 18 – kryzhov, Alexeysun. 19 – Antonio Guillem. 20 – Photographee.eu, Daisy Daisy, Monkey Business Images. 21 – Africa Studio, WAYHOME studio. 22 – Lopolo. 23 – paulaphoto. 24 – ESUN7756, Phakin S. 25 – Thaninee Chuensomchit , antoniodiaz, Dragon Images. 26 – Bukavik. 27 – GMonkey Business Images, cristovao. 28 – Daisy Daisy, Monkey Business Images. 29 – Andrey_Popov. 30 – VGstockstudio, Monkey Business Images. Images are courtesy of Shutterstock.com, unless stated otherwise. With thanks to Getty Images, Thinkstock Photo and iStockphoto.

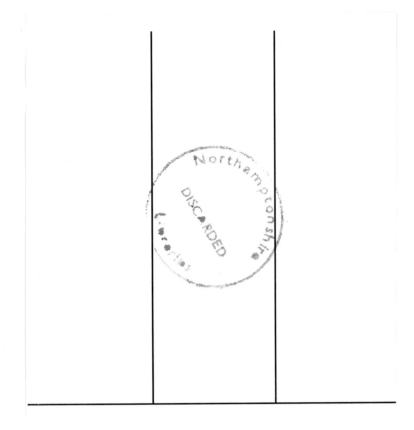

CONTENTS

Words that look like **THIS** are explained in the glossary on page 31.

WHAT IS OCD?

OCD stands for obsessive compulsive disorder and it is a type of anxiety disorder. Anxiety is the word we use to describe feelings of worry and fear. Everybody feels anxious from time-to-time, but people with an anxiety disorder like OCD find it hard to control feelings of anxiety and it stops them from doing the things they want to do.

IN EVERYDAY LANGUAGE, HAVING AN 'OBSESSION' USUALLY MEANS BEING REALLY INTERESTED IN SOMETHING. FOR PEOPLE WITH OCD, AN OBSESSION IS A FEAR THAT TAKES UP A LOT OF THINKING TIME.

OCD has two main parts: obsessions, which are thoughts and fears that cause anxiety, and compulsions, which are the actions or **RITUALS** that someone with OCD does in order to get rid of these thoughts and fears. If you have OCD, your brain finds it harder to let go of worries and fears. They might go round and round in your head for a very long time. This is why OCD thoughts get called obsessions. Compulsions can include things such as repeating words or movements, counting, checking, tapping, ordering and cleaning.

Many people have worrying thoughts and do certain actions to try and make themselves feel better. For example, some people check that they have locked the front door many times when they leave their house. This doesn't always mean they have OCD. OCD obsessions and compulsions take up a lot of time, affect your day-to-day life and make you more anxious in the long run.

AROUND 1 IN EVERY 100 CHILDREN HAS OCD. THAT MEANS THAT IF YOU HAVE OCD, THERE IS LIKELY TO BE SOMEONE ELSE IN YOUR SCHOOL THAT HAS IT TOO.

OCD can be mild or **SEVERE** but all people with OCD experience obsessions and compulsions. OCD can be difficult to deal with but it can get better. It can be treated, usually by a doctor or a **THERAPIST**, who will teach you ways to cope with your anxious thoughts and compulsions.

Some people even reach a point where they don't perform any compulsions anymore. Because OCD is an anxiety disorder, learning more about what anxiety is and how to deal with it can help people to cope with conditions like OCD.

OCD IS CONSIDERED A MENTAL HEALTH CONDITION BECAUSE IT IS A HEALTH CONDITION THAT AFFECTS THE MIND.

WHAT IS ANXIETY?

Anxiety is an emotion that makes us feel frightened or stressed. Sometimes it can be a helpful emotion. For example, if you are anxious about a test, it can motivate you to work hard and do well. However, too much anxiety might make you too scared to even take the test at all. This isn't helpful and it can make you feel very **OVERWHELMED**.

Think back to a time when you felt scared. You might have had a racing heart, shaky legs or a stomach ache. Maybe you felt very hot or a bit dizzy. You might even have felt like crying or shouting. These are all **SYMPTOMS** of anxiety that happen in our bodies. They are nothing to worry about and will go away once you feel calm again.

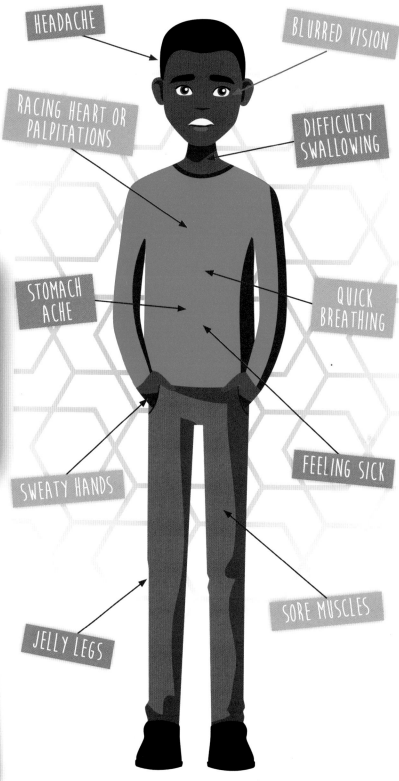

HEADACHE

BLURRED VISION

RACING HEART OR PALPITATIONS

DIFFICULTY SWALLOWING

STOMACH ACHE

QUICK BREATHING

FEELING SICK

SWEATY HANDS

SORE MUSCLES

JELLY LEGS

The Worry Cycle

Sometimes these **PHYSICAL** symptoms can spark a cycle of worry because they can make you believe that there is something wrong with you, or that you are unwell.

A WORRYING THOUGHT POPS INTO YOUR HEAD AND MAKES YOU FEEL ANXIOUS.

I'm not feeling very well. What if I'm sick in front of everybody?

I really am going to be sick!

My stomach feels bad.

YOU THINK YOUR WORRIES MUST BE TRUE WHICH CAUSES YOU TO WORRY EVEN MORE.

FEELINGS OF ANXIETY AFFECT YOUR BODY.

PANIC ATTACKS

Occasionally, a worry cycle can lead to something called a panic attack. A panic attack is a very intense feeling of anxiety that comes on all of a sudden. People who are experiencing a panic attack might:

- Worry that they are going to die
- Feel like shouting or crying
- Feel out of control of their body

Panic attacks can be scary but they can't hurt you, and they only last for a short amount of time. Having someone sit with you and help you calm down can help stop a panic attack.

FIGHT, FLIGHT,
FREEZE!

Panic and worry happen because of something called the fight, flight, freeze response. This is a full body response to anxiety that helps give us the energy to face up to our fears (fight) or run away from them (flight). The third option, freeze, happens when we feel so overwhelmed that it feels like we are stuck-to-the-spot.

The fight, flight, freeze response happens because of a whole system of messages being sent from your brain to your body.

HYPOTHALAMUS

AMYGDALA

1. THE FIRST MESSENGER IS CALLED THE AMYGDALA (SAY: A-MIG-DUL-A). THIS PART OF YOUR BRAIN IS RESPONSIBLE FOR WARNING YOU ABOUT DANGER.

2. THE AMYGDALA TELLS ANOTHER PART OF YOUR BRAIN, CALLED THE HYPOTHALAMUS, ABOUT THE DANGER. THE HYPOTHALAMUS SENDS A MESSAGE TO YOUR BODY TO TELL IT TO RELEASE A **HORMONE** CALLED ADRENALINE (ALSO CALLED EPINEPHRINE).

3. ADRENALINE TELLS YOUR HEART TO BEAT FASTER AND YOUR LUNGS AND MUSCLES TO WORK HARDER.

SCIENTISTS THINK HUMANS **EVOLVED** THE FLIGHT, FIGHT, FREEZE RESPONSE BECAUSE, IN THE PAST, BEING ABLE TO FIGHT OR RUN AWAY FROM WILD ANIMALS HELPED OUR **ANCESTORS** TO SURVIVE.

8

The problem with the fight, flight, freeze response is that our worries aren't always about things that we can fight or run away from. Often they are much more complicated than that. When we have no use for the energy that adrenaline gives us, it can make us feel very unpleasant and can cause some of the many physical symptoms of anxiety described on page 6.

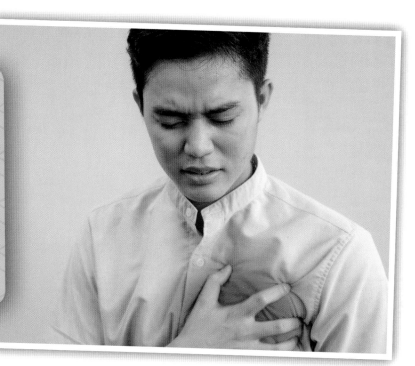

For example, it might cause us to hyperventilate (say: high-per-VEN-ti-late). This is when we breathe in too much air. This can make us feel dizzy and lightheaded but usually goes away after calming down. Our hearts beating quickly may cause us to have fast or irregular heartbeats called palpitations. Again, these are often uncomfortable but are nothing to worry about. The release of adrenaline can also affect your **DIGESTIVE SYSTEM** by making you feel sick or like you need to go to the toilet. It can also make you feel sweaty and your vision might blur.

OBSESSIONS

Obsessions are the thoughts and fears that people with OCD experience. Some people's OCD makes them worry that something bad will happen to them or someone they love. Other people's OCD might make them worry that they are in some way a bad person. People can have many different obsessions but OCD obsessions tend to have common **THEMES**.

Some of these are:

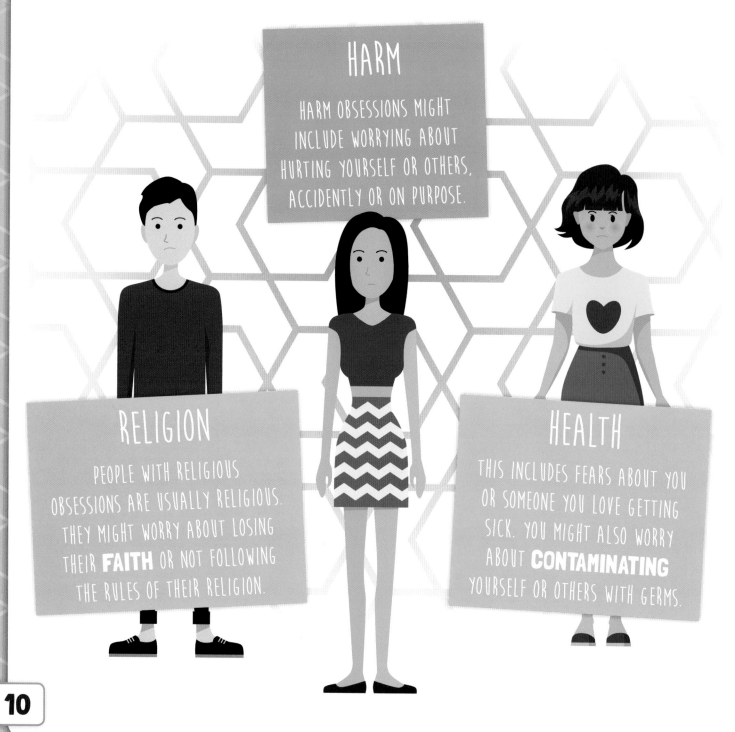

HARM

HARM OBSESSIONS MIGHT INCLUDE WORRYING ABOUT HURTING YOURSELF OR OTHERS, ACCIDENTLY OR ON PURPOSE.

RELIGION

PEOPLE WITH RELIGIOUS OBSESSIONS ARE USUALLY RELIGIOUS. THEY MIGHT WORRY ABOUT LOSING THEIR **FAITH** OR NOT FOLLOWING THE RULES OF THEIR RELIGION.

HEALTH

THIS INCLUDES FEARS ABOUT YOU OR SOMEONE YOU LOVE GETTING SICK. YOU MIGHT ALSO WORRY ABOUT **CONTAMINATING** YOURSELF OR OTHERS WITH GERMS.

These are just some of the things that OCD obsessions might focus on. Some people with OCD have just one obsession whereas others have many different ones. Children with OCD might experience different types of obsessions as they grow up. Although these can be difficult to deal with, they can be overcome with the help of a therapist or doctor who can help people understand and deal with the anxiety caused by the obsessional thoughts.

EACH TIME YOU DEFEAT A FEAR, OVERCOMING NEW ONES BECOMES MUCH EASIER.

MAGICAL THINKING

IF YOU HAVE MAGICAL THINKING OCD, YOU MIGHT WORRY THAT YOU CAN MAKE SOMETHING BAD HAPPEN JUST BY THINKING ABOUT IT. YOU MIGHT THINK YOU CAN ACCIDENTALLY CAUSE A **NATURAL DISASTER**, OR CHANGE THE FUTURE.

SOCIAL

THESE KINDS OF OBSESSIONS ARE ABOUT WHAT OTHER PEOPLE THINK OF YOU. YOU MIGHT FEAR DOING SOMETHING EMBARRASSING OR SOMEONE FINDING OUT SOMETHING PRIVATE ABOUT YOU.

MORALITY

MORAL OBSESSIONS MIGHT MAKE YOU WORRY ABOUT BEING A BAD PERSON. YOU MIGHT TRY TO BE WELL-BEHAVED ALL THE TIME, BUT STILL FEEL LIKE YOU ARE BAD.

INTRUSIVE THOUGHTS

People with OCD have a lot of **INTRUSIVE** thoughts related to their obsessions. Intrusive thoughts can be doubts, images, urges and even memories that come into your head uninvited and make you feel uncomfortable or scared. For example, someone with OCD who is scared of getting in trouble at school might get intrusive thoughts about their teacher shouting at them. Their OCD might even make them worry that they will lose control and do something against the rules.

MANY PEOPLE DESCRIBE THEIR OCD AS BEING LIKE A LITTLE VOICE IN THEIR HEAD TELLING THEM THINGS AND MAKING THEM WORRY. THIS IS NOT REALLY A VOICE, BUT IS OCD THOUGHTS.

OBJECTS, PLACES AND SITUATIONS THAT SET-OFF INTRUSIVE THOUGHTS ARE OFTEN CALLED 'TRIGGERS'.

People with OCD like this are very unlikely to actually do anything wrong. OCD obsessions – especially harm and morality obsessions – often give people intrusive thoughts about things that are against their beliefs and **VALUES** and it can make them question who they are as a person. Because of this, intrusive thoughts are hard to ignore.

A lot of the time, intrusive thoughts are not that scary on their own, but they are scary because of what we think they might 'mean'. For example, you might get a thought about pushing your friend over in the playground. This thought isn't necessarily frightening, but you might worry about what it means. Does it mean you are a bad person? Are you violent, or a bully?

These questions frighten us because they go against what we believe about ourselves. If we believe we are a kind person, thoughts about hurting a friend make us doubt that belief. However, the very fact these thoughts worry people with OCD means they are likely to be very kind and thoughtful people. Everybody has thoughts about things that are bad, rude or selfish but that doesn't mean that we are these things. You might think you are the only person who has these thoughts, but that's not true either. It is important to remember that thoughts are very random and, just because we think something, it doesn't mean it's true.

DIFFERENT FEARS

There are two types of fears: rational fears and irrational fears. Rational fears are about things that are likely to happen and are in your control. For example, you might worry about failing a test at school. It makes sense to worry about this a little bit, as it will motivate you to work hard and do well. Irrational fears are about things that are less likely to happen and are out of your control. For example, being scared of being struck by lightning would be considered an irrational fear because, although it is scary, it is very unlikely to happen and it is completely out of your control. Sometimes rational fears can become irrational. For instance, some people are scared of dogs. It makes sense to be scared of an angry, snarling dog; this could hurt you so your fear tells you to stay away and keeps you safe. An irrational fear would be being afraid of all dogs – even friendly ones that are on a lead.

People with anxiety disorders are more likely than others to have irrational fears or to have rational fears that become irrational. Having OCD can be like being extremely superstitious. Have you ever avoided walking under a ladder, or been worried about breaking a mirror in case it brings bad luck. This is what having OCD can be like. Even though you know that you probably won't have bad luck if you do these things, the belief is still hard to ignore. For someone with OCD, their mind makes its own rules and superstitions; it tells people that by doing a compulsion, they can prevent something bad from happening.

Every time someone with OCD does a compulsion and nothing bad happens, their mind sees it as proof that doing the compulsion works. This means they might have to do more and more compulsions in the future. For example, someone might clean their kitchen over and over so they don't get **FOOD POISONING**. This works because they don't get ill. However, they were unlikely to get ill in the first place.

COMPULSIONS

For someone with OCD, it feels like the only way to get rid of intrusive thoughts is to perform an action or ritual. Sometimes compulsions are related to the worrying thought. For example, someone with a fear of contamination might wash their hands over and over until they're sore. Other types of compulsions aren't related to the worry. For example, someone's OCD might tell them that jumping up and down on the spot a certain number of times will stop something bad from happening to them. The problem with compulsions is that they only make people feel better for a short amount of time. The more times you do a compulsion, the stronger the worries get and the more compulsions you have to do next time. It goes round and round in a cycle.

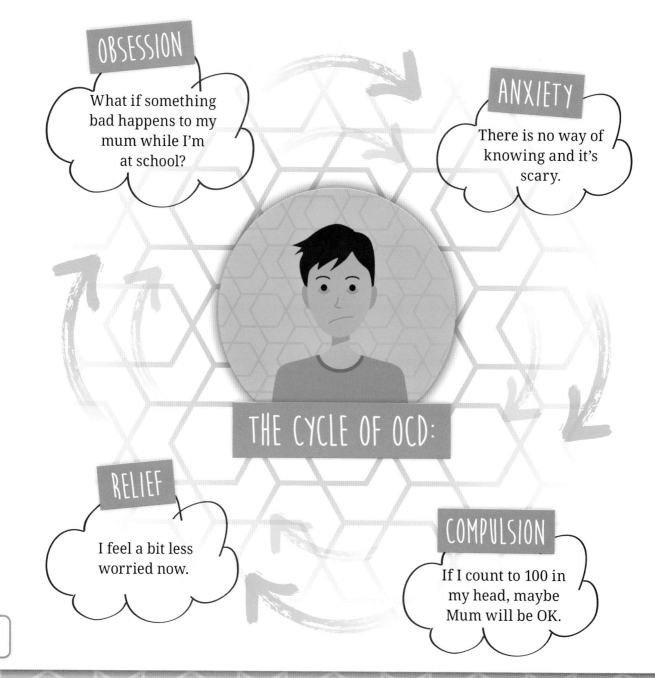

OBSESSION
What if something bad happens to my mum while I'm at school?

ANXIETY
There is no way of knowing and it's scary.

THE CYCLE OF OCD:

RELIEF
I feel a bit less worried now.

COMPULSION
If I count to 100 in my head, maybe Mum will be OK.

Types of Compulsions

Like obsessions, there are also many types of compulsions.

Checking compulsions might include checking something you wrote for mistakes, checking that doors are locked, or calling a family member to check they are OK.

Ordering and tidying compulsions might include tidying and rearranging objects and making sure things are **SYMMETRICAL**.

Cleaning and washing compulsions often involve washing your hands and body or cleaning your clothes and toys over and over.

Touching and tapping compulsions might mean touching objects a certain number of times or until it feels 'just right'.

Counting and repeating compulsions might involve counting to certain 'lucky' numbers or repeating everyday actions like switching a light switch on and off.

Mental rituals are compulsions that you do inside your head. This might mean saying lucky words or phrases silently to yourself.

REASSURANCE compulsions make you ask someone to reassure you over and over that nothing bad is going to happen.

Avoidance compulsions make you want to avoid things that make you anxious. For example, avoiding going out any time it's raining because you are afraid you will be struck by lightning.

My name is Lola and I have OCD, which makes me worry about lots of different things. I didn't know I had OCD at first; it just felt like there was a part of my brain telling me what to do. Whenever I was worried, the OCD part in my head made me do something like open and shut doors and climb in and out of my bed. If I didn't do it, it felt like all my worries would get out of control.

I didn't like having to go upstairs to bed because I felt like I had to climb the stairs over and over. Mum used to tell me off – she thought I did it because I didn't want to go to bed. In the mornings, I used to worry that something bad would happen at school. It took me a long time to get ready. I had to take my shoes off and put them on again lots of times before it felt OK.

When I was at school, I couldn't open and shut doors because I was worried I'd look strange, so my brain told me to do other things like rub out my work and write it all over again. It meant I couldn't finish my work on time and sometimes I had to stay in at break times to get it finished.

Mum took me to see a therapist and I told him that it felt like there was a bully in my head telling me what to do. He told me about OCD and now I know the things my brain tells me to do are compulsions.

My therapist helped me make a list of all the worries that come into my head when I want to do a compulsion. Now we are going to try to stand up to the OCD and say no to some of the things it tells me to do. This feels frightening but I know with my counsellor's help I can do it.

TREATING OCD

There are many different ways of treating OCD, from relaxation techniques to talking about your feelings with a therapist. One of the most common treatments for OCD is something called CBT, which stands for cognitive behavioural therapy. This might sound very serious at first, but it is simply a type of therapy that helps people to break the cycle of intrusive thoughts and compulsions.

OCD makes people believe that if they don't do a compulsion, something bad will happen. This is why it is very frightening and difficult for someone to just ignore a compulsion. It can feel like not scratching a really bad itch. CBT helps people to understand their thoughts and fears and then to challenge some of the OCD thoughts and compulsions. For example, if someone is very scared of getting poorly from germs and their compulsion is to wash their hands over and over, then a therapist might help them to learn about their fear. They might help them learn more about germs and how they work.

COGNITIVE MEANS THOUGHTS AND FEELINGS.

Thinking about a fear can be very scary at first but it can help someone with OCD realise that it is very unlikely that their fear will come true. This causes OCD to lose some of its power. Instead of trying to make the thought go away by doing a compulsion, a therapist might help their patient to think about the **WORST-CASE SCENARIO** that could happen if they didn't do it. In time, this scenario might not feel as scary.

CBT also helps people to face their fears by challenging their compulsions. After a while, you might feel strong enough to ignore the urge to do a compulsion. This helps to prove that not doing the compulsion won't cause anything terrible to happen. Every time you don't do a compulsion and nothing bad happens, it makes the OCD 'voice' a little quieter.

CBT IS A **GRADUAL** PROCESS. NO ONE CAN MAKE YOU DO SOMETHING THAT YOU DON'T WANT TO DO OR DON'T FEEL READY FOR.

CAN YOU THINK OF SOMETHING THAT YOU USED TO BE SCARED OF BUT AREN'T ANYMORE? WHAT HAPPENED TO MAKE YOU NOT SCARED?

SENSORY GROUNDING

Facing your fears head-on can be very stressful. Luckily, there are many relaxation techniques that we can use to calm down when anxiety becomes too much. One of these is called sensory grounding. Sensory grounding is all about using your senses to focus on your surroundings which can make you feel calmer.

1. START BY TAKING SLOW, DEEP BREATHS. BREATHE IN FOR THE COUNT OF FOUR AND OUT FOR SIX.

2. LOOK AROUND YOU. CAN YOU LIST FIVE THINGS THAT YOU CAN SEE? CAN YOU SEE PEOPLE AROUND YOU? WHAT COLOUR IS THE FLOOR?

3. LISTEN UP. WHAT ARE FOUR THINGS YOU CAN HEAR? IT MIGHT BE PEOPLE TALKING, OR CARS DRIVING OUTSIDE.

4. PAY ATTENTION TO YOUR BODY. WHAT CAN YOU FEEL? PERHAPS YOU CAN FEEL YOUR CLOTHES ON YOUR SKIN. WHERE ARE YOU SITTING? CAN YOU FEEL THE FURNITURE UNDERNEATH YOU?

Balloon Breathing

Learning how to take slow, deep breaths is a very important part of relaxation. One way of doing this is to practise balloon breathing.

1. IMAGINE THERE IS A BALLOON IN YOUR BELLY. TAKE A DEEP BREATH THROUGH YOUR NOSE AND IMAGINE THAT YOU ARE FILLING UP YOUR BALLOON.

2. BREATHE OUT SLOWLY THROUGH YOUR MOUTH AND IMAGINE THAT YOU ARE DEFLATING THE BALLOON IN YOUR BELLY. MAKE SURE TO SQUEEZE ALL THE AIR OUT.

3. KEEP PRACTICING BREATHING LIKE THIS. TRY COUNTING TO FOUR WHILE YOU **INHALE** AND TO SIX WHILE YOU **EXHALE**.

BALLOON BREATHING CAN BE USED TO HELP YOU GET TO SLEEP TOO!

TOP TIP!
IF YOU CAN, WHY NOT TRY LISTENING TO SOME RELAXING MUSIC THROUGH HEADPHONES WHEN YOU ARE DOING THIS.

23

CASE STUDY: ARCHIE

My name is Archie and earlier this year I was **DIAGNOSED** with OCD. I had always had a little voice in my head that made me worry, but it got much worse when Mum gave birth to my baby brother, George. I didn't want a new brother at first and I felt jealous of him when he was born.

Because I felt jealous, my mind kept telling me that it meant I wanted to hurt my brother. I knew this wasn't true but it made me really scared. I kept having thoughts about dropping him or making him cry. I worried that I was a bad brother and what my mum would think of me if she knew what was going through my head. After a while, I started doing things to prove the voice wrong. I started hiding things that I thought might hurt George and every time a bad thought came into my head, I had to say "I don't want to hurt my brother," over and over again.

I started saying it just once or twice, but soon I had to say it lots of times every day and, if I was somewhere where I couldn't say it, I had to think it inside my head and tap the back of my hand. I liked being at school because I was far away from George, but I hated going home and would cry a lot at pick-up time.

Mum noticed something was wrong and took me to see a **PSYCHOLOGIST** called Amy. It is her job to help children like me. She told me I had OCD and that some people's OCD makes them worry that they might hurt someone, but that these thoughts are never true. She said the fact I was worried in the first place shows that I would never do anything to hurt my brother.

I now know that the things I do to stop the thoughts are called compulsions. With Amy's help, I stopped doing some of my compulsions and nothing bad happened. I still get horrible thoughts sometimes but I know that Amy will help me to fight them.

FIGHTING BACK

OCD intrusive thoughts are often very **EXAGGERATED** and it's easy to find yourself believing them. Just like you might handle a bully by thinking of a good comeback, it is important to have good comebacks for your OCD thoughts too. One way we can do this is by using the three C's: catch, check and change.

When we have an intrusive thought, it is important to catch it and **EXAMINE** it rather than accepting it or doing a compulsion to get rid of it. Next, we can check the thought and weigh up how true it actually is. Where is the **EVIDENCE** that this thought is true? Lastly, we can change the thought to something more rational. By reminding ourselves to catch, check and change our thoughts, we can start to challenge obsessions and compulsions.

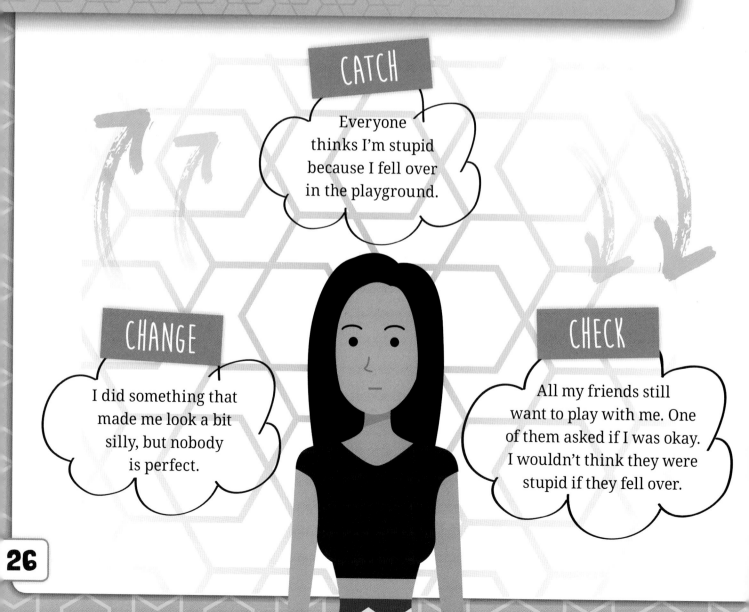

CATCH

Everyone thinks I'm stupid because I fell over in the playground.

CHECK

All my friends still want to play with me. One of them asked if I was okay. I wouldn't think they were stupid if they fell over.

CHANGE

I did something that made me look a bit silly, but nobody is perfect.

Using a Scale

Sometimes we find ourselves in situations where we can't talk to someone straight away or there are lots of other people around, for example, in a classroom. In situations like these, it can help to tell someone you trust, like a teacher, about how you feel using a scale of one to ten; ten being really anxious and one being really relaxed. You can then simply say, "I'm feeling about a seven," or even just hold up seven fingers. You can even do this in your own head and focus on using some of the relaxation techniques we learnt earlier to bring those numbers down.

If no one is around to talk to, there are lots of things you can say to yourself to help you challenge your OCD. Next time you are feeling anxious, try telling yourself the following things:

I HAVE BEEN BRAVE BEFORE AND I CAN BE BRAVE AGAIN.

I MIGHT FEEL SCARED BUT FEELINGS CAN'T HURT ME.

MY THOUGHTS ARE JUST THOUGHTS. JUST BECAUSE I THINK THEM, IT DOESN'T MEAN THEY'RE TRUE.

DOING THE THINGS YOU LOVE

One of the best ways to tackle anxiety is to do more of the things that make you happy because it can help distract you from worrying thoughts. People have lots of different hobbies and interests, from playing games and watching films to reading books and drawing pictures. Whatever your hobbies are, make sure to regularly do the things you enjoy.

Getting Active

Getting active can really help to reduce anxiety because it uses up some of the adrenaline produced by our bodies during the fight, flight, freeze response. You can exercise by yourself or with other people. When you exercise, chemicals called endorphins are released in your brain which makes you feel happy. Some people with OCD find that exercise gives their body something to do and can help distract them from some of their compulsions.

TAKING PART IN TEAM SPORTS CAN HELP YOU MAKE FRIENDS!

OCD

"A LITTLE OCD"

From time-to-time, you might hear people use the word OCD incorrectly. You might have heard people describe themselves as "a little OCD" when they mean that they like to have things clean and tidy. This is not the same as OCD, which is a serious anxiety disorder.

Using the word OCD incorrectly like this is harmful because it makes something that is really difficult for people seem silly or even like a good thing to have. It also means that children and adults who have OCD but do not have tidying or cleaning compulsions may not realise they have it and may not get the help they need.

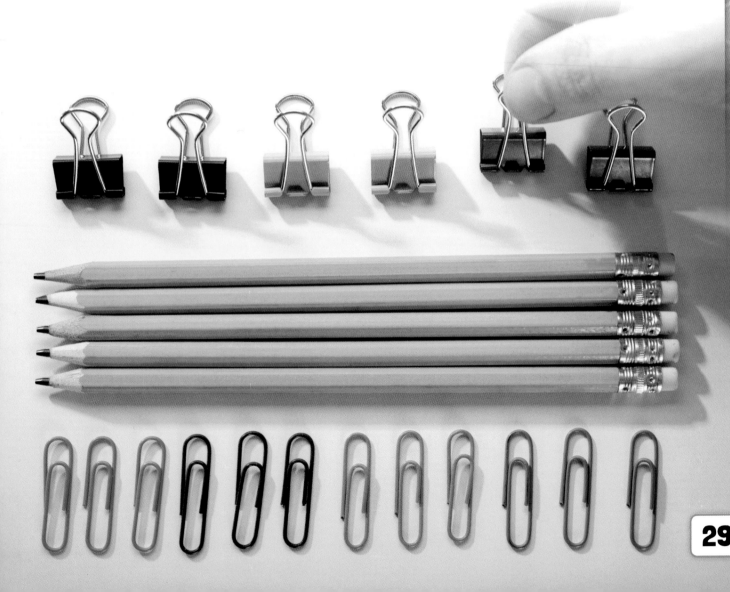

SPEAKING UP

OCD often makes people worry about things that are embarrassing, frightening or difficult to talk about. Many children with OCD are nervous to tell people about their compulsions in case people don't understand or think that they are 'weird'. This **STIGMA** can make people who have OCD feel very alone. However, it is important to remember that having OCD does not make you weird or weak in any way. Children with OCD are actually very brave because, unlike many other children and even adults, they have had to learn how to face up to their fears much more quickly.

NO MATTER HOW SCARY OR STRANGE YOU THINK YOUR WORRIES ARE, IT IS ALWAYS BEST TO TELL AN ADULT YOU TRUST ABOUT THEM. OCD IS A VERY WELL-UNDERSTOOD CONDITION AND YOU ARE NEVER ALONE.

Talking about our mental health is just as important as talking about our physical health. OCD might make you feel like you can't talk about your feelings or that no one will understand, but this is not true. We would tell someone when our body is hurting, so we should also tell people when our mind is hurting too. Talking about how we are feeling can do amazing things for our mental health and well-being.

GLOSSARY

ANCESTORS	persons from whom one is descended, for example a great-grandparent
CONTAMINATING	making something unclean
DIAGNOSED	when a disease or illness is identified by a doctor
DIGESTIVE SYSTEM	a group of organs whose job it is to absorb food into the body and turn it into energy
EVIDENCE	the available facts or information that are used to decide whether or not something is true
EVOLVED	gradually developed over a long time
EXAGGERATED	when something is made to be bigger or more important than it actually is
EXAMINE	to closely inspect and think critically about something
EXHALE	breathe out
FOOD POISONING	illness caused by eating food full of harmful bacteria
GRADUAL	at a slow pace
HORMONE	a chemical in your body that tells cells what to do
INHALE	breathe in
INTRUSIVE	unwelcome and coming without invitation
FAITH	belief in a religion and a god or gods
MORALITY	a person's sense of what is right and what is wrong
NATURAL DISASTER	a natural event that causes great damage to an area
OVERWHELMED	when emotions feel too much to handle
PHYSICAL	relating to the body
PSYCHOLOGIST	someone who studies the human mind and can help people with mental health conditions
REASSURANCE	comforting words or actions which make someone feel less worried or scared
RITUALS	routines or sets of actions that are performed over and over
SEVERE	(of something bad) serious, very great or intense
STIGMA	a set of negative and often unfair beliefs about something
SYMMETRICAL	matching on both sides
SYMPTOMS	things that happen in the body suggesting that there is a disease or disorder
THEMES	broad ideas or subject areas
THERAPIST	a person who is specially trained to treat mental health conditions
VALUES	principles that are important to people
WORST-CASE SCENARIO	the worst possible outcome

INDEX